101 Challenges

Become the Best You

Tad Mitchell

Thank you to the WellRight team who served as guinea pigs testing each of the challenges. Thank you to my editors: Emily, Renee, and Tricia. Thank you to our reviewers. Thank you to Tamara who refined the artwork and did the layout. Thank you to all who provided feedback.

Tad

Disclaimer: Information in 101 Challenges is for educational purposes only and is not meant to substitute for the advice of a medical professional. You should consult with a health care professional before starting any diet, exercise, or supplementation program.

First Edition

Printed in U.S.A.

ISBN 978-0-9964417-3-5

More information about the book can be found at www.101Challenges.com.

When I entered the world of wellness in 2013, I had no idea of the personal change that I was about to undergo. I joined WellRight to build software. Gamification was all the rage, but what frustrated me was that all the games were just that—games. Games and rewards got people to engage (and customers to renew their contracts), but there was no lasting wellness.

We quickly gravitated toward habits as the solution, specifically wholistic habits. In WellRight's early days, we experimented using challenges to build new habits. Sometimes our experimental challenges failed, but most of the time we were able to tweak them and make them work.

After several successes, our health coach and I came up with an even greater challenge, just for us: Eat Clean—No empty calories. The goal was to eliminate sugar, refined grains, and fried foods for 30 days. It seemed so hard that I didn't feel right asking the whole company to do it. Our health coach was far more optimistic and started inviting people individually to participate. Then somewhat of a miracle happened. One by one, our employees accepted the challenge. To my amazement, most of them successfully completed the challenge! While no one continued to eat clean perfectly, everyone's diet has been permanently improved as a result.

The fitness and nutrition challenges were great, but that was just the beginning. The mind was our next frontier. One of my favorite mental well-being challenges was the Gratitude Journal— List 90 things you're thankful for (3 a day). Another favorite was Be Positive—No complaining (say something positive each time you catch yourself complaining). Again, people didn't achieve perfection from these challenges, but they were permanently changed for the better—and so was our company culture.

After participating in dozens of challenges, I can see myself changing, and doing so more quickly than I would have imagined. I'm frustrated that I didn't know how to put the life-changing power of habits to work for me earlier in my life. Three years of good habit building has made my life so much more enjoyable and our company culture so much stronger. My wish is to help everyone change themselves for good, one habit at a time.

Introduction

Whether you are an individual trying to improve your personal well-being or a health professional designing wellness programs for large populations, it's important to ask yourself this question: "If you aren't building habits, what are you doing?"

You are the sum of your habits. The way to redefine yourself is to change your habits. You can go on a crash diet and pounds will be lost, but unless new habits are developed in the process, the weight will eventually return. Such is life. In anything you do, unless you build habits, you will always revert to your former self.

So, forming new habits is great, but where do you start, how far should you reach, and how can you make it fun? That's where challenges come in. Properly designed challenges provide a framework for habit formation. Challenges have a goal, a beginning, and an end. Challenges make building habits approachable and doable. They turn the overwhelming subject of self-improvement into baby steps that anyone can do.

How to Use This Book

To change yourself or your organization for good:

      1. Pick a challenge.

      2. Do it.

      3. Repeat.

It's that simple. Sometimes the habit will stick. Sometimes it won't. Either way, you'll be moving in the right direction—becoming a better you.

Habits

A habit is defined as something we do automatically, without thinking. We do hundreds of things each day without thinking. Think about the last time you drove your car. When you arrived, you didn't even remember stepping on the gas, looking in the mirror, or turning your blinker on. You were on autopilot. Instead of concentrating on the tasks of driving, you were probably thinking about something completely unrelated.

For most of what we do, we are on autopilot, otherwise we couldn't do half the things we do. The brain can only focus on a few things at once. Think back to when you were learning how to drive. There were so many things you had to do simultaneously that sometimes you could easily forget to do one of them, like turning on your blinker or checking your blind spot. The learning process was stressful. It's the same as we develop new habits. If we try to juggle too many new habits at once, it will become too difficult and we won't build any.

Developing a healthy lifestyle is a lot like learning to drive a car. It can take years to build the right habits, but once you do, you can maintain your health without giving it much thought. Imagine what else you could accomplish if taking care of your health happened automatically.

How to Build a Habit

Below is the 6-step process for building habits from my book, *21 Habits: A Wellness Survival Guide.*

1. **Believe It.** Pick a habit that you are excited about and believe in.

2. **Shrink It.** Break the habit down into something that is so easy that you can't not do it.

3. **Trigger It.** Choose a trigger for the habit, ideally something that already happens.

4. **Prepare for It.** Get the tools needed and prepare your environment for success.

5. **Track It.** Write down each time you do your habit so you can see your progress.

6. **Be It.** Make the habit part of your identity.

The great thing about challenges is that they bundle up these six steps into a single, fun package, which makes it easy for you to focus on forming new habits.

Challenges

Challenges are a great tool for building habits. First of all, they have a limited duration—allowing you to try something without committing to it. Challenges also require you to track your progress—helping you to succeed. Furthermore, they can be done in a group—providing a social experience, friendly competition, and peer support. Finally, they are fun—everyone likes a challenge!

How to Design a Challenge

While challenges can be powerful, they can also fail miserably. Below are some guidelines that will help you design your own challenges. Who knows what you'll come up with?

- **Make Everyone a Winner.** Challenges should allow all participants to achieve the goal and associated reward. It's okay to track who is leading, but it's best to not reward the leader(s)—they already have their reward.

- **Encourage Daily Activity.** It's much better if a challenge fosters a daily activity rather than meeting a goal that can be done in a couple marathon sessions. For example, instead of making the goal to walk 150,000 steps, make the goal to walk 5,000 steps each day for 30 days.

- **Level the Playing Field.** In an effort to make a challenge "challenging," sometimes it becomes too hard for some participants—often the ones who need it the most. Try tracking minutes instead of steps, or do a nutrition challenge instead of a fitness challenge.

- **Allow for Exceptions.** If someone falls short, there should be a way for them to stay in the challenge. Allow for a set number of exceptions during the period of the challenge, or allow people to earn exceptions by doing something extra like exercising for an extra half hour.

- **Keep It Simple.** In an effort to create the perfect challenge, the requirements can sometimes get overcomplicated. The simpler a challenge is, the more likely it is to be successful.

- **Make It A Challenge.** People like to be challenged. If the challenge is too easy, it's not appealing. On the other hand, if it's too hard, people won't attempt it. Find the right balance between achievable and challenging.

- **Choose the Right Duration.** If a challenge is too long or too short, its impact may be lessened. Most of the challenges in this book are 30 days in duration, long enough to experience the benefits and build a habit, but not too long to lose interest.

1,000**Strong**

1,000 reps

The 1,000 Strong Challenge invites you to complete 1,000 reps of one strength exercise over 30 days (an average of 33 reps per day). There's no need for a gym membership to reach this goal. You can strength train at home or even at the office using exercises like push-ups, squats, lunges, and planks. Try doing several reps each time you take a bathroom break or a few every time you get a drink. Without even breaking a sweat, you'll easily get your 33 reps in each day and you'll sharpen your thinking by getting your blood pumping. To get the most out of this challenge, pick an exercise that requires some effort to get to that 1,000 mark.

Strength training is a great way to increase metabolism and boost energy during the day and help you sleep better at night. When you take the time to build strength, especially as you grow older, you'll see that it's not just about looking better. Strength training combats the natural decline in muscle mass and bone density as you age. It even helps you manage the stress in your life. The 1,000 Strong Challenge is a baby step to better health. Maybe you'll enjoy strength training enough to keep going after the challenge!

Air1,000

Exercise outside for 1,000 minutes

The Air 1,000 Challenge invites you to exercise outside for 1,000 minutes in 30 days (an average of 33 min/day). You can do any exercise you want, as long as it's outside. Go for a run. Take a walk. Mow the lawn. Work in your garden. Wash your car. Meditate on your patio. Just do something active outdoors and enjoy the fresh air and sunshine (hopefully). Do your exercise before or after something you already do, like lunch or dinner, to help remind you to get outside.

While exercising outdoors can increase your energy level and help you feel more alive and refreshed, nature also has a calming effect. In fact, spending a few minutes outside clears your head and helps you think better. Whatever you choose to do, make the most of it and take in all the sights, sounds, and smells around you. You might even run into a friend or neighbor. Stop and chat. You can still count the time as long as you are outside.

Arctic500

Walk outside for 500 minutes

The Arctic 500 Challenge invites you to walk outside during the winter for 500 minutes in 30 days (an average of 17 min/day). You can walk fast or slow, alone or with a friend. Even shoveling snow or sledding works. The point is to do some type of physical activity outside when you would most likely rather stay indoors.

During the winter, it's easy to fall into a routine where you run from indoors to a heated car and back again, avoiding the outdoors altogether. Getting outside in the winter, especially during the daytime, is important for your mind and your body. It can replenish your depleted vitamin D reserves, help you avoid weight gain, and chase off the winter blues. Don't let winter beat you. Bundle up and make enjoying winter a part of your normal routine. Most importantly, be careful if it's slippery!

Classy**Gym**

10 gym classes

The Classy Gym Challenge invites you to attend 10 classes at the gym over the next 30 days. You choose which classes you'd like to attend. Attend the same class each time or different ones. The class can be high energy (like spinning) or relaxing (like meditation)—make sure to pick something at your current fitness level. If you've never tried this before, the goal is to see if gym classes work for you. If you have taken gym classes in the past, the goal is to get you going again. If you're a regular, the goal is to get you to try a class you've never tried before.

Group fitness classes are a great way to jumpstart your fitness program. You don't need to figure out what to do—just show up. The instructor will make sure you do a proper warm-up, cool-down, and everything else in between. Classes also keep you more accountable. Simply having a scheduled time can make it easier to get out and exercise, and if you have already paid for the class, you're less likely to miss it. Best of all, classes are fun: they play great music, the instructors pump you up, you're with others, and you can bring a friend. Give it a try and see if group classes are right for you.

FiveK

Complete a 5K

The Five K Challenge invites you to support your favorite cause and complete a 5K run/walk. Committing to an organized race is a great motivator, and if you're already a regular competitor, there's always the challenge of beating your best time. If you aren't already in the habit of running or walking regularly, start at a comfortable level, pace yourself, and work up to going the full 3.1 miles.

The 5K distance is ideal for promoting overall fitness. It can help you develop a combination of endurance, speed, and strength, with little risk of injury. You can train for a 5K without taking up much time from your normal life. To top it off, the social benefits are great: you can challenge a friend or family member to train with you. Sharing the 5K experience will be more fun and you can even take a photo together at the finish line!

Flex Time

Stretch for 100 minutes

The Flex Time Challenge invites you to stretch for 100 minutes over the next 30 days (or 3–5 min/day). Stretching is a natural impulse that is good for you—especially if you work at a desk. The key is to pay attention to that urge to loosen up and use it to your benefit. It's easier to form a habit if you add stretching to something you already do like a workout or a morning break.

When you stretch, it increases your blood flow and elasticity, and decreases tightness in your tendons and muscles. When you feel emotionally stressed and tense, a short stretching break can do wonders. Simply lifting your arms up overhead and creating length in your body can give you a much welcomed break. Just stretching for a few minutes each day is all it takes to complete the Flex Time Challenge.

Heavy**Metal**
Strength train for 250 minutes

The Heavy Metal Challenge invites you to do 250 minutes of strength training during the next 30 days. You can reach your goal with only two or three 30-minute strength training sessions per week. If you'd like to train more often, be sure to alternate muscle groups to give your muscles time to recover. Most people think that strength training requires lifting heavy weights, but body weight exercises like push-ups, pull-ups, sit-ups, or squats build strength, too. That means there's no need to purchase weights or a gym membership to complete this challenge. You can research strength training sets and sequences online to design your own routine or you can work with a certified trainer to design a routine that is best for you. Variety is important.

Strength training is your ticket to good health and overall fitness. It will give you better coordination, improved posture, and stronger bones. As the body ages it loses muscle mass and gains fat. Strength training combats both. Best of all, strength training pumps you up. There's nothing like the feeling after a good strength training workout. Give it a try and see if you like it.

Move|t

5,000 steps a day

The Move It Challenge invites you to take 5,000 steps a day for 25 days out of the next 30 days. It's not hard to walk 5,000 steps in a day. It's only 2.5 miles (4 kilometers). The trick is doing it every day (or almost every day). That's the habit this challenge is trying to build—a minimum amount of activity each day. Moving will help you feel better, look better, and be happier!

You can make this challenge a lot easier if you have a step tracker. Use a simple pedometer, which can cost less than $10, or you can download a free pedometer app onto your phone. Don't be intimidated by this goal if you're not very active. Depending on your environment, you may actually take 5,000 steps a day with your normal activities. If this is the case, great! If not, find ways to add steps to your day. The trick may be the days that are not your norm, like weekends or when traveling. Whatever your environment, moving 5,000 steps a day will have a positive impact on your life.

Stair**Master**
300 flights of stairs

The Stair Master Challenge invites you to step it up—to be exact, step up 300 flights of stairs in 30 days (10 flights a day). Sorry, down doesn't count. The goal is to build the habit of taking the stairs as much as you can instead of the elevator or escalator. Taking the stairs when you have a choice is a great habit to get into. It gets your blood pumping (cardio) and your muscles working (strength) at the same time.

Stair climbing requires bursts of energy and burns calories fast, so you get a high payback in a short amount of time. Stairs are everywhere and cost nothing to use. Often using the stairs is just as fast or faster than using the elevator. So why not get in some exercise instead of standing around waiting? Go ahead, step it up!

StandUp

Get up every hour

The Stand Up Challenge invites you to get up and move around every hour—8 times a day, for 30 days. That may sound like a lot, but the average office worker spends nearly six hours a day sitting at a desk. Now, that's a lot! This kind of sedentary lifestyle can't simply be countered by a gym session after work. Studies show that the answer is to stand up and move around for a few minutes every hour of your work day. Stretch at the same time for an added bonus.

The biggest trick to being successful with this challenge is figuring out a reliable trigger to remind you to stand up. For some, simply standing up at the top of the hour works. Others use alarms. Drinking water steadily throughout the day works too, keeping you going for refills and bathroom breaks all day long. If you are stuck in a meeting, you can still stand up. Standing up gets your blood flowing and keeps you alert. Standing up regularly can reduce your risk of obesity, cardiovascular disease, type 2 diabetes, and cancer. So stand up for your health!

TeamPlayer

Play on a sports team

The Team Player Challenge invites you to play one season on a sports team. Soccer, softball, basketball, volleyball—even dancing counts. Choose whatever sport you want. If you can't find a team in your area, start your own team. Playing on a team makes staying fit second nature. You're so focused on the game, you forget how hard you're working.

Whether it's a serious league or just for fun, playing on a sports team puts the fun into fitness! It also keeps you accountable, knowing that your team needs you. Team sports demand strategy, spontaneity, creativity, and other mental talents that solo workouts don't require. You're also likely to make some great friends along the way!

Walk There

120 miles

The Walk There Challenge invites you to walk 120 miles within 30 days (4 miles a day). Think about your normal patterns each day and look for opportunities to walk more. Can you make walking part of your commute? Can you park farther away from a store or restaurant? Can you take a lap around your office building on a break during the day? You could fit any of these things into your daily routine and continue to do them even after the challenge is over. Walking more throughout the day is a much better approach than taking extreme hikes or runs that you know you may never repeat once the challenge is over.

Walking is free and easy. Regular, brisk walking can help you sleep better at night, reach or maintain a healthy weight, prevent a variety of diseases, and improve your balance, coordination, and mood—so many benefits for such a simple thing! The faster, farther, and more frequently you walk, the more benefits you will experience.

Walkie Talkie

Walk and talk for 500 minutes

The Walkie Talkie Challenge invites you to walk with someone else for 500 minutes during the next 30 days (17 min/day). The easiest way to meet this health-boosting challenge is to find a friend or family member to be your walking partner. If you walk together three times a week (40–45 minutes each time), you'll easily reach your 500 minutes. Shorter walks are fine, too—just adjust your schedule. If a friend or relative isn't available, try talking on the phone while you walk. Talking with another person while you walk helps you focus on the conversation rather than on walking, which is great because your workout will fly by.

Not only are walking and talking fun, but they are two of the best things you can do for your health. Walking invigorates your mind and works your muscles. Talking helps you stay mentally healthy and prevents your problems from getting the best of you. Creating a habit of walking and talking will improve the quality of your life both now and into the future. If you're having a hard time getting motivated to exercise, walking and talking might be just what you need.

WalkMeet

8 walking meetings

The Walk Meet Challenge invites you to hold eight walking meetings during the next 30 days, two a week. Not all meetings can be done effectively while walking, but some can. In fact, getting up and moving around actually heightens brain activity, stimulating thoughts you might not otherwise have. A change in environment can also activate the brain. So, the next time a meeting calls for creative thinking, ditch your office and hit the road.

If you have a lot to cover in your meeting, make of list of topics beforehand to help keep you on track, but make sure you allow enough time to fully explore all the ideas that arise. If the weather is nice, walking outside will give you the additional benefits of fresh air and sunshine, but walking indoors works, too. Walking to a restaurant could turn a lunch meeting into a walking meeting. You may enjoy these walking meetings so much that you'll keep doing them long after the challenge ends!

WorkoutBuddy

10 workouts with a friend

Fitness

Mental

The Workout Buddy Challenge invites you to workout with a friend 10 times in the next 30 days. Yes, working out with the same person is part of the challenge. The stronger a relationship is, the more beneficial it is. Most of us know workouts are healthy, but you may not realize how beneficial solid relationships are for your health. They can actually impact your health as much as a regular workout routine, just in different ways.

Working out with a friend can be much more fun than working out alone, and there are also several other benefits. First, a workout buddy holds you accountable to show up in the first place. Your workout will go quickly because you'll enjoy being together. You can also encourage and help one another. If you are lifting weights, you can spot each other. If you are running, you'll probably run longer and faster because you won't want to hold your partner back. Having a workout buddy may be just the boost you need!

Bean Power

Make 5 recipes with beans

The Bean Power Challenge invites you to make five different recipes that contain beans (legumes) during the next 30 days. For most of us this is a true challenge. Bean burritos are easy enough, but where do you go from there? It's worth the effort to incorporate more beans into your diet because from a nutritional standpoint, beans are hard to beat. Beans provide a good source of complex carbohydrates, including fiber, along with protein to help us feel full and energized. Hopefully this challenge will help you make beans a regular part of your diet.

Canned beans are convenient and tasty, but be sure to rinse them to reduce the amount of gas they cause. For dry beans, throw out the soaking water for the same result. Many bean dishes can be made within 30 minutes, such as: black bean soup, lentil stew, red beans and rice, chili, bean salad, hummus, and bean dip. Pressure cookers are great for cooking beans very quickly. You can also prepare a quick bean recipe in a crockpot in the morning and come home later to a hot, delicious, nutritious meal. Hopefully this challenge will help you make beans a regular part of your diet.

Beat**Sweets**

No sugar

The Beat Sweets Challenge invites you to eliminate sugary foods from your diet for 30 days. Yes, you heard that right—no sugar for 30 days. At first, this may sound daunting—if not impossible—but once you get away from sugar for a few days, it gets easier and you will feel better. When you stop eating sugar, you may even lose weight, sleep better, and feel more energized. After a month without sugar, you may be surprised at how wonderful natural foods taste.

Eating too much sugar has been associated with many serious diseases, including obesity, type 2 diabetes, and cardiovascular disease. Sugar contains ample calories and minimal nutritional value. Despite maintaining or gaining weight from eating so many calories, you may actually be starving your body of important nutrients. If you do slip, don't despair. You can redeem yourself by exercising a half hour more than you usually do. This will give you the flexibility to enjoy a piece of birthday cake, but will hopefully keep you in check so you get right back to your no sugar challenge.

Caffeine**Free**

No caffeine

The Caffeine Free Challenge invites you to go without caffeine for 30 days. That means no coffee, no tea, no caffeinated soda, and no energy drinks. Decaf coffee, herbal tea, and chocolate are fine. You may have wondered what life would be like without caffeine. Now's your chance to give it a try. See if you can face life on your own without the crutch of caffeine.

Although caffeine can give you an energy boost, it also blocks the messages to your brain telling you that you're tired. Your body needs rest and if you continually deprive your body of that rest, it could cause mental and physical problems including anxiety attacks, difficulty sleeping, and trouble recovering from workouts. If you are dependent upon caffeine to get through your day, you may experience headaches and fatigue for the first few days of the challenge. Hang in there, take a nap if you can, and drink extra water—it will get better within a few days.

Deep**Fried**
No fried foods

The Deep Fried Challenge invites you to go without deep-fried foods for 30 days. This includes anything cooked in hot oil like french fries, chips, fried chicken, donuts—pretty much all the good stuff. Deep-fried foods sure are tasty, but as you probably know, they're not good for you. This is your chance to see how your body feels without deep-fried foods. You may even like the feeling.

Deep-fried foods have two to three times the calories of the non-fried version. For example, a fried chicken breast has roughly 325 calories, while a grilled chicken breast has roughly 105 calories. Even worse, frying oil has typically been chemically altered to make it last longer at high temperatures, creating an oil that our bodies have difficulty metabolizing. Eat foods that are roasted, baked, grilled, boiled or fresh—there are so many healthy, great-tasting alternatives to deep-fried foods. If you slip up, don't give up. Exercise an extra half hour and call it good.

Eat**Clean**

No empty calories

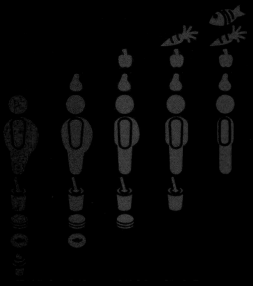

The Eat Clean Challenge invites you to eliminate sugar, fried foods, and refined grains from your diet for 30 days. This may be the hardest nutrition challenge of all. The goal is to eat more nutrient dense foods and eliminate empty calories (foods that are high in calories and low in nutrition). To make this challenge a little bit easier, 70% dark chocolate and honey are allowed. If you do need to make an exception, you can exercise for an extra 30 minutes to make up for it. This gives you a little flexibility on occasion, but won't allow you to get too far off track.

Sugary foods include most dry cereals, sweetened yogurt, cookies, ice cream, muffins, etc. Fried foods are those cooked in oil, like donuts, french fries, fried chicken, and potato chips. Refined grains include white rice, white bread, regular pasta, and anything that is made with white flour. Don't fret about the small things. If you have a little ketchup made with sugar or eat a soup thickened with white flour, that's fine. Focus on the big picture while you strive to eat clean.

The Eat Plants Challenge invites you to limit yourself to 30 servings of meat during the next 30 days and to eat more plant-based foods. Meat includes beef, pork, and poultry. To make things easier, you don't have to count fish, which may have more health benefits than other types of meat. Meat is good for you in small amounts, but many of us eat far too much meat, which can have negative effects on our health. People who eat mostly plant-based foods and only occasionally eat meat, have a lower risk of heart disease and other chronic diseases. A serving of meat is three ounces (cooked) or about a half cup, so a big steak is actually several servings of meat.

If you are eating one serving of meat per day, combined with the rest of your diet, you are most likely getting enough protein. Other good sources of protein include beans (legumes), eggs, dairy products, and nuts. Many cultures live healthy lives with no meat at all, mostly by including beans and grains in their diet. When planning your meals, try thinking of the meat as a condiment or side dish instead of the main dish and you should be fine.

Five**Alive**

150 fruits or vegetables

The Five Alive Challenge invites you to eat 150 servings of fruits and vegetables in 30 days (5 per day). A serving is about 1 cup for most fruits and vegetables and 2 cups for leafy greens. They can be cooked or raw, fresh or frozen. Five servings a day may seem like a lot, so you may need to plan ahead to make sure you get them all in. If you only eat four one day, you can eat six the next day to catch up. If you're not a fan of fruits and vegetables, smoothies or soup may be delicious alternatives. You can easily squeeze three to four servings into a single smoothie. Soup is the hot and savory version of a smoothie and is a simple way to eat lots of vegetables.

The great thing about eating fruits and vegetables is that even though five servings is a lot of food, it's not a lot of calories. In fact, fruits and vegetables are the foods with the highest nutrition-to-calorie ratio, protecting your body from illness and disease like no other food. You should eat your fruits and vegetables both cooked and raw. Cooking may destroy certain nutrients, but it makes others available or easier to digest. Whichever method you choose, eating plenty of each will give you a healthier, happier body.

Food**Tracker**

Track what you eat

The Food Tracker Challenge invites you to track everything you eat for the next 30 days. You can use the health app that comes with your phone, the app that comes with your fitness tracker, or you can download a popular food tracker app. The goal of the challenge is to increase your awareness of what you eat and how many calories different foods contain. This simple challenge will probably help you make better food choices for the rest of your life.

One benefit of tracking everything you eat is that it makes you more aware of how often and how much you eat (which may be more than you care to realize). Since you may not want to log any unhealthy foods, you will probably choose better options and lose a little weight over the 30-day challenge. This will help you eat less and become more in tune with how much food your body really needs. If eating too much isn't your problem, maybe it's eating too many unhealthy foods. Tracking what you eat will allow you to discover your unique eating patterns and help you bridle them for better health. Try it yourself and see.

Go**Slow**
Put your fork down

Nutrition

The Go Slow Challenge invites you to put down your fork (or spoon) between bites whenever you dine for the next 30 days. If you're eating something you hold in your hands, like pizza, set it down on your plate between bites. Chew thoroughly, enjoying the texture and flavors as you eat. The goal is to help you learn to eat more slowly. When we eat quickly, we have a tendency to overeat because it takes a while for our brains to register that we're full. Savoring every bite will actually help you feel satisfied sooner and enjoy your meal more.

Studies have shown that eating more slowly and chewing food longer is likely to reduce the number of calories you consume. In addition, it helps your body digest food, improving the absorption of vitamins and minerals. Perhaps the most important benefit of putting down your fork between bites is that it will give you a chance to enjoy the taste of the food along with the company of your family or friends. You'll enjoy each meal more as you get into the habit of eating slowly.

GoGreen
20 salads

The Go Green Challenge invites you to enjoy 20 salads in the next 30 days. Salads are a great way to incorporate vegetables into your diet. Feel free to get creative and try different types of salads, like coleslaw, carrot salad, or broccoli salad. Even if the salad isn't your entire meal, a nice salad at the beginning will start to fill up your stomach with low-calorie vegetables before you get to the main course. Just be careful with the toppings! Adding too much dressing, croutons, meat, or cheese to a nutritious salad can sabotage your effort to eat a healthy meal.

Vegetables are densely packed with nutrients and provide much-needed fiber for your diet. Eating raw vegetables also helps your body naturally clean toxins from your organs for a healthier digestive system. If you top your salad with healthy fats like olives, avocados, and nuts, you'll enjoy even more health benefits.

Go**H2O**

Choose water

The Go H2O Challenge invites you to replace one or more beverages (soda, juice, coffee, alcohol, etc.) with water for 30 days. You choose how aggressive you want to be by deciding which beverages you will give up. Drinking water is the best way to hydrate your body. In fact, there's no need to drink anything besides water—unless it's for pleasure.

Did you know that drinking water can help you lose weight? When you are properly hydrated, you feel hungry less often. It can also help reduce fatigue and headaches. An easy way to get into the water-drinking habit is to take a water bottle with you everywhere you go. When you go to a restaurant, be sure to ask for water. Always keep water close by and drink away!

Nutrition

Financial

HelloSunshine

10 days of sunshine

The Hello Sunshine Challenge invites you to get out in the sun 10 days (10–15 min/day) during the next 30 days. Ideally, you'll do this challenge in the winter or spring when your vitamin D levels may be at their lowest. When the sun hits your skin, it creates vitamin D_3, which you can't produce on your own. Vitamin D_3 is vital for a strong immune system and strong bones, so it's crucial that you get ample exposure to sunshine whenever you can. There is even evidence that sun exposure can help you sleep better at night.

We all know too much exposure to the sun can cause skin cancer and premature aging of the skin, but many people aren't aware that diseases and depression can also result from not enough sunshine. It's definitely important to find the right balance. Roll up your sleeves and go outside so your skin can get a healthy dose of sunshine; you will feel happier and healthier.

Kitchen Closed

No eating after dinner

The Kitchen Closed Challenge invites you to avoid eating or drinking anything other than water after dinner for 25 of the next 30 days. Clean up right after dinner, turn off the kitchen lights, and stay out of that area for the remainder of the evening. To help you remember, brush your teeth after you leave the kitchen for the night.

Eliminating snacking after dinner reduces your total calories for the day. It also gives your body time to digest your food before going to bed, improving the quality of your sleep and reducing the occurrence of heartburn. This challenge also eliminates late night caffeine and the resulting need to use the bathroom in the middle of the night. Not only will you wake up feeling rested, you'll have a clean kitchen to boot!

Magic**Bean**
15 servings of beans

The Magic Bean Challenge invites you to enjoy 15 servings of beans (legumes) during the next 30 days. One serving of beans is only one-half a cup of cooked beans, so it's possible to eat two or more servings in a single meal. Beans satisfy your hunger and make you feel full longer, reducing the urge to snack between meals. Beans are an excellent source of protein, complex carbohydrates, and fiber. In fact, a serving of beans supplies nearly 8 grams of fiber, which is important for healthy digestion. Eating more beans truly can be magical for your health.

Beans have a bad rep because they can cause flatulence, but if you chew them thoroughly, your digestive system will have an easier time metabolizing them. Also, when you include beans as a regular part of your diet, your body happily adjusts, reducing the worry of embarrassing side effects. Try adding beans to your salad, soup, or meal a few times a week and you should be able to easily meet the Magic Bean Challenge.

Naturally**Sweet**

Eat fruit for dessert

The Naturally Sweet Challenge invites you to eat fruit for dessert for 30 days. That's right. No sugary, processed, high-calorie desserts for a month—just pure and natural fruit. During the challenge you may discover many varieties of sweet and flavorful fruit. Enjoy the full, aromatic sweetness of a natural treat that is unrivaled by the overpowering taste of refined sugar.

While fruit does contain sugar, it has much less by volume than sugary treats. For example, a half cup of strawberries has 3.5 grams of sugar, contrasted with 15 grams in a half cup of strawberry ice cream. Fruit is also full of vitamins, antioxidants, fiber, and water—all good things your body needs. When you feel like snacking on cookies or candy, choose fruit instead. The more you develop this habit and stay away from refined sugars, the more you will enjoy each fruitful bite.

Once ^{N} Done

No seconds

The Once N Done Challenge invites you to avoid second servings of food for the next 30 days. Not taking seconds is a simple way to control how much food you eat. Often, overeating is something we do automatically. The food is there, it's delicious, everyone else is eating—so even though we really aren't hungry any more, we continue eating. By simply committing to only one serving ahead of time, you can fill your plate sensibly and enjoy your food. Perhaps the easiest, best way to meet this challenge is to place your napkin on your plate as soon as you're finished eating.

Resisting seconds is a powerful, yet simple step toward better health. Overeating can cause obesity, diabetes, chronic illness, and depression. Limiting yourself to one serving may help you feel more in control and be more likely to make other healthy choices. This simple challenge may take some mindfulness at first, but once your body gets used to not eating more than you need, you will feel content eating just one serving.

Right**Weigh**

Weigh yourself monthly

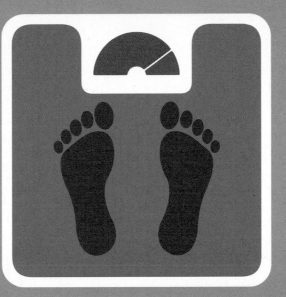

The Right Weigh Challenge invites you to weigh yourself at least monthly for an entire year. Being aware of your weight can help you make sure that you don't get too far off track with variations in eating or exercise.

When you do weigh yourself, do it on the same day of the week, at the same time, using the same scale. This limits inaccuracies due to normal daily and weekly fluctuations in your weight. Be sure to record your weight each time. It can also be interesting to take measurements of certain areas like your waist and hips that tend to change with weight fluctuations. Just the simple act of weighing yourself regularly will help you stay focused on maintaining a healthy weight.

SmoothSailing

Make 10 smoothies

The Smooth Sailing Challenge invites you to make 10 smoothies in the next 30 days, or 3–4 smoothies per week. Caution! Depending on how you make them, smoothies can contain as many calories as a burger and fries. Stay away from using ice cream, sweetened yogurt, and fruit juices in your smoothies. Let fresh or frozen fruit do the sweetening. Incorporate as many nutrient-rich, low-calorie vegetables as your palate can take. Made properly, smoothies can be a super quick, super nutritious meal. (Sorry, purchased smoothies don't count.)

Smoothies aren't for everyone, but they do provide some unique advantages. They are easy to make and quick to eat if you are short on time. A smoothie is a great way to incorporate fruit, vegetables, and other nutritious foods in your diet. If you use frozen fruit, you won't have to shop as often or worry about your fresh fruit going bad. If you don't like veggies, but know you need the nutrients, try blending a flavor-neutral option like spinach into your smoothie. If you need a little extra protein, no problem—just add a few nuts or seeds (or a natural protein powder). Who knows? Maybe smoothies will become part of your regular routine. Happy blending!

SnackAttack

Don't eat between meals

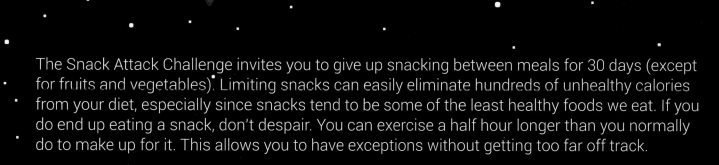

The Snack Attack Challenge invites you to give up snacking between meals for 30 days (except for fruits and vegetables). Limiting snacks can easily eliminate hundreds of unhealthy calories from your diet, especially since snacks tend to be some of the least healthy foods we eat. If you do end up eating a snack, don't despair. You can exercise a half hour longer than you normally do to make up for it. This allows you to have exceptions without getting too far off track.

The best part about the Snack Attack Challenge is that if you're a grazer, you will still have the option to snack all you want—just focus on fruits and vegetables. You'll find that fruits and vegetables satisfy your hunger better and do not have the addictive properties of most snacks. Just be sure to keep the snack simple: no ranch dip with your vegetables or caramel with your apples. Focus on enjoying the fruit's or vegetable's pure, undiluted flavor.

SoupKitchen

Make 5 soups

The Soup Kitchen Challenge invites you to make five different soup recipes in 30 days. Generally speaking, homemade soup is healthy because it contains nutritious vegetables and beans, which are sometimes hard to work into your diet. The broth fills your stomach, reducing the chances of overeating. Making a big batch of soup will also save you time later on, as soup often tastes better the second day, and you can freeze the soup in smaller portions for a quick meal later on.

Be aware that not all soups are good for you. Ready-made and restaurant soups are often loaded with sodium, which over time can impact your blood pressure and kidneys. Also, cream-based and cheese-based soups can have a huge amount of calories. Making your own soup at home lets you control the amount of salt, and you can use milk or a non-dairy substitute instead of cream. If you like a smoother texture, blend your soup before serving. Blending is also a great way to sneak in vegetables you or your family normally wouldn't eat.

Table Time

Eat at a table

Nutrition

Mental

The Table Time Challenge invites you to eat all your meals and snacks at a table for 30 days. Sorry, your desk doesn't count. The idea is to set aside time specifically for eating without other distractions like computers, phones, or television. Doing this will help you be more aware of how much you are eating and will give you a moment to savor your food. If you are able to eat with others, that's even better. Conversation fills the soul and makes you eat slower—giving your brain some time to recognize that you're full and reducing the chances of overeating.

In today's fast-paced world, eating slowly seems like a waste of time. So we eat while we work, we eat while we drive, and we eat while we relax watching TV or browsing the Internet. The problem with this is that we don't realize what or how much we're eating because we're focused on something else. By taking time to sit at a table, we consciously focus on what we are eating. If we aren't really hungry, we won't stop to sit down and eat. When we do, however, it's much easier to control the quantity. Best of all, when we focus on eating, we take the time to savor one of the simplest pleasures in life.

UnRefined

No refined grains

The Un Refined Challenge invites you to not eat refined grains (white rice, regular pasta, and anything made with white flour) for 30 days. Refined grains have little nutritional value compared with the high amount of calories they provide. When grains are refined, the bran (the outer covering) and the germ (the seed-like portion) are removed, along with the vitamins, minerals, and dietary fiber that they contain. The remaining white flour or rice that you eat is quickly digested by the body (like sugar), potentially causing blood-sugar imbalances, inflammation, overeating, and weight gain.

On the other hand, whole grains, which are rich in fiber and other nutrients that help slow digestion and the absorption of sugar into your bloodstream. The result is long-lasting energy that keeps you fueled for hours. This challenge may seem limiting at first, but there are plenty of tasty whole-grain foods to enjoy. Try wild rice or brown rice instead of white rice, and whole-wheat pasta instead of regular pasta. Check the label on any food made with flour—look for 100% whole grain and if you see "enriched" on the label, it means it's refined.

Skip Chips

No chips

The Skip Chips Challenge invites you to avoid eating any kind of chips for 30 days. Nobody can deny that chips are delicious, but we all know they aren't healthy. Yet, we can't stop eating them because chips are addictive. Most are made of fat, salt, and carbs—all things our body craves. Food designers use this craving to make us want to eat more. The excessive amounts of fat, salt, and carbs contribute to high cholesterol, high blood pressure, and weight gain. Don't get caught in these deceptive traps: "Baked is better," "sea salt," or "vegetable chips." These chip variations aren't healthy either.

Food makers blend chemicals, taste, mouthfeel, and fat ratio to lure you into eating one chip after another. This makes them hard to resist—but with determination, victory can be yours, especially if you avoid taking that first bite. Swap empty chip calories for food choices that will actually contribute to good health and nutrition, like fresh fruit and yogurt, vegetables and hummus, plain popcorn, or nuts.

Top Chef

10 new recipes

The Top Chef Challenge invites you to try making 10 new recipes in the next 30 days. In general, home-cooked food is healthier than packaged or restaurant food because you control what goes into it. The goal of this challenge is to help you expand your cooking repertoire so you can make home-cooked meals more common in your life. You could try 10 new recipes for cookies, but why not stick with the spirit of the challenge and pick healthy recipes that you would consider eating regularly?

If you don't know where to start, think of something you like to eat but don't know how to cook. Browse through an old cookbook or ask a relative for a favorite family recipe. Check out instructional videos online if you'd rather see a demonstration before trying something new. Once you've learned to cook some new recipes, invite guests over to try your creations. You can also double a recipe so you can freeze some for a second meal.

WaterBottle

Keep water at your desk

The Water Bottle Challenge invites you to keep a water bottle or a glass of water at your desk all day for the next 30 days. If you don't work at a desk, keep a water bottle at your virtual desk— car, couch, or whatever it may be. As soon as you drink the last drop, refill it immediately. Having water readily available will make it easy for you to drink plenty of it each day.

Getting enough water removes toxins, lubricates joints, softens skin, reduces headaches, increases bowel regularity, and much more. A good indicator that you are well hydrated is when you urinate every 4–5 hours. So grab your water bottle, fill it up, and drink it while you work!

5Questions

30 question-based conversations

The 5 Questions Challenge invites you to ask five or more questions of someone each day for the next 30 days. Whether you're the type of person that can carry a conversation or the type that does more listening, asking questions can improve the depth of your conversations. Don't feel pressured to fire away five questions in a row. Rather, ask them whenever it seems appropriate throughout the conversation. In fact, don't even bother counting how many questions you ask (the exact number doesn't matter). The point is to focus on the conversation and find out more through questions.

Dale Carnegie said, "You can make more friends in two months by becoming interested in other people than you can in two years by trying to get other people interested in you." When you show another person that you are interested in what they have to say, it makes them feel valued and respected. You don't have to be a skilled journalist to ask a good question. Even asking someone what they plan to do over the weekend or a question to follow up on the last conversation you had will make them feel like you care.

Be**Grateful**

List 90 things you're thankful for

The Be Grateful Challenge invites you to write down three things you are grateful for each day for 30 days. By the end of the challenge, you will have a list of 90 different things that you are thankful for. It only takes a minute each day but can change your whole outlook on life. Expressing gratitude can improve your physical and mental health, and even help you sleep better.

Recognizing the good things in your life helps you step away from your problems for a moment and think less about what you don't have. Thinking about what you do have builds self-esteem brings more satisfaction and joy into your life. Feeling a sense of gratitude leads to a positive mental state that is free of emotions like envy, frustration, resentment, and regret. Focusing on the good things in your life will help you build self-esteem and have a more mindful and joyous quality of life. Give gratitude a try and see what this simple habit can do for you.

Mental

Be**Positive**
No complaining

The Be Positive Challenge invites you to stop complaining for 30 days. For some, this may seem impossible. You may feel like you can't say anything. Your mind might be filled with complaints that seem completely valid to release. Don't be discouraged. Tackle these thoughts one at a time. You'll eventually conquer this habit. Until you do, when you slip, restate the complaint as a positive thought and call it progress.

The world we live in is a reflection of our own energy. When we give out positive thoughts instead of complaints, we find that the world around us becomes a more pleasant, enjoyable place to live in. This alone is good for our health and well being. What's more, when we exude a positive attitude, we attract people instead of repelling them—making it a better and healthier experience for all of us. Think of the people you enjoy spending time with most—chances are they have a positive outlook on life.

BloodDrive

Give blood

Save a life
Give blood

The Blood Drive Challenge invites you to donate blood one time. Donating blood once may not build a habit, but hopefully it will break the ice for future donations. Did you know that when you donate blood, you can help as many as three people and sometimes even save a life?

Donating blood can also be a good way to keep an eye on your cardiovascular health (with no cost to you). A nurse will check your pulse, blood pressure, body temperature, hemoglobin, and more. This can sometimes shed light on issues you didn't even know about. Since your blood says a lot about your health, keeping tabs on it can alert you to a health issue before it becomes life threatening. Best of all, there's nothing like the feeling you get when you help someone else.

Mental

Book Worm

Read for 1,000 minutes

The Book Worm Challenge invites you to read a book for 1,000 minutes over 30 days, an average of about 30 minutes a day. Digging into good books can literally add years to your mental health. Reading can protect your brain from Alzheimer's disease and other forms of dementia. Reading can also help you feel less stressed and more positive.

For this challenge, you need to actually read, not listen. While audiobooks are convenient, the process of converting the symbols on a page into meaning increases your brain power (cognitive processing skills)—it's like a workout for your brain. Even better, reading helps your whole body relax, giving your mind a break from day-to-day pressures. Choose a good book and curl up in a comfy spot, relax your body, and exercise your mind!

BreatheDeep

40 breathing sessions

The Breathe Deep Challenge invites you to slow down and breathe deeply twice a day, five days a week, for the next four weeks. Focused breathing can help you become calm when you feel anxiety, like right before a job interview or giving a presentation. Research has shown that slowing your breathing lowers levels of anxiety, calming your brain and enabling you to deal with daily challenges more effectively. Taking slow, deep breaths can also help you notice and enjoy the moment you're in and give you a nice mental break.

You can do any breathing exercise you choose, but here's a simple one that will only take a couple of minutes: Count to 4 as you breathe in. Hold for 4 counts. Breathe out for 4 counts. Hold for 4 counts. Repeat 4 or more times. Breathe in through your nose and out through your mouth. Let your belly expand. Relax your body as you breathe. Give it a try and see how good it feels.

Mental

Brain

Exercise your mind for 300 minutes

The Brain Teaser Challenge invites you to play brain teasers for 300 minutes over the next 30 days, or an average of 10 minutes a day. Some examples include crossword puzzles, word searches, Sudoku, and memory games. You can choose any brain teaser you like. Today there are even mobile apps with games and puzzles specifically designed to increase your brain's capacity. The idea is to exercise your mind which, just like a muscle, becomes stronger with use.

While many consider games to be simply entertainment, puzzle games can increase the brain's ability to learn. Puzzles, letter games, and other brain teasers help you develop your logic skills and recognize patterns, which can help you solve life's daily challenges. Some puzzles improve spelling and language skills. Others increase your ability to concentrate or be creative. Not only will exercising your brain make you smarter and more effective today; it will also help prevent decline in your cognitive abilities as you age.

Bucket List

Check off one item

The Bucket List Challenge invites you to complete one item on your bucket list. If you don't have a bucket list (a list of things you want to do before you die), your first project is to make one. After that, choose one thing from your bucket list that you can feasibly accomplish this year and put a plan in place to do it.

We often think of bucket list items as being lofty goals for someday down the road. We may even wonder if we'll ever actually do it. When you actually fulfill a goal from your bucket list, you will increase confidence in yourself and your ability to accomplish a goal. Who knows what series of events you may set in motion by accomplishing this one thing? Even if you don't end up accomplishing the goal like you'd planned, you'll still be closer than you were before you started. Go ahead, live one of your dreams!

Mental

Chill**Pill**

Relax for 500 minutes

Mental

The Chill Pill Challenge invites you to relax for 500 minutes during the next 30 days (17 min/day). Do something you enjoy, something that is not part of your usual routine. You would think relaxing is something everyone can do naturally, but some of us find it more challenging than others. Some feel it is a waste of time, but this couldn't be further from the truth. Relaxing is like sharpening your saw. You will be much more efficient and effective after you take some time to relax and refresh.

The first thing to do is to figure out what is relaxing for you. Different people find different activities relaxing. Some might unwind best while gardening, taking a walk, writing, or having a conversation with a friend. Listening to music or taking a quick power nap might work better for you. There's no need to wait until the end of the day (or when you're truly exhausted) to chill. Start your day with some reading. Take a walk with a friend at lunch. You'll quickly find that taking time to relax makes you feel better and perform better when you are not relaxing.

Clean Desk

Declutter your desk

The Clean Desk Challenge invites you to clean off your desk 5 days a week for the next four weeks. The purpose of this challenge is to get you in the habit of setting aside time near the end of your workday to clean up your space and make it nice and organized so you'll have a clean canvas the next morning. If you occasionally hit a time crunch and have to leave a few things sitting out, that's okay, but do your best to keep your desk decluttered during the day and allow time for straightening things up before you go home.

A clean workspace will free your mind to be more creative. You will be able to find the things you need, complete tasks more efficiently, and think more clearly. When others stop by your desk or workspace, they'll see your organization as a reflection of you and your capabilities. It may take a little while to clean your desk the first time, but it won't be hard to maintain. As you have a moment, go ahead and organize your drawers, too. Give a decluttered desk a try; you'll like the feeling!

Mental

Colo ful Life

Color for 300 minutes

Mental

The Colorful Life Challenge invites you to spend about 10 minutes a day coloring for the next 30 days, totaling 300 minutes. Remember when you used to enjoy coloring as a child? Nothing has changed. Coloring is still enjoyable. In fact, coloring has been proven to reduce stress, increase focus, and put you in a state of consciousness like meditation.

Psychologists say coloring engages both the logical and creative parts of the brain, slows heart rate and respiration, and loosens muscles. The amygdala—the part of the brain that detects fear and spurs emergency responses—gets a rest, which has a significant calming effect. After coloring a little each day for a month, you should feel more relaxed and patient—and will have a little more color in your life.

Connect40

40 conversations

The Connect 40 Challenge invites you to have 40 meaningful conversations with different people in 30 days. Call an old friend. Talk to your neighbor. Strike up a conversation with a stranger. Phone your mom or a grandparent. Having strong social ties can help you live a longer, healthier life. Even just a good chat with your hairdresser or someone on the train can give your mood a boost and give you both a reason to smile.

Talking with others helps you learn new things and see life from a different perspective. We tend to smile and be cheerful when we talk with others. Talking with a family member or close friend (by phone or in person) can make us feel loved and less lonely. A conversation can also help us think through problems, which can diffuse stressful situations we are facing. There's something powerful and energizing when two people connect.

Mental

Create|It

Express yourself for 500 minutes

The Create It Challenge invites you to spend 500 minutes creating something during the next 30 days (17 min/day). Play music, write, dance, draw, garden—even organize a room or a tackle a do-it-yourself home repair. Being creative stimulates your mind, giving you a sense of identity and accomplishment.

Pablo Picasso said, "Art washes away from the soul the dust of everyday life." This is true not just for art, but for any form of creating. While drafting the Declaration of Independence, Thomas Jefferson took breaks to play his violin. Creating music—or anything else—helps unlock both sides of the brain, which can be both calming and invigorating. Whether you choose to make pottery, build a deck, or even build a snowman, creating can be one of the most satisfying activities you do.

Daily**Plan**

Plan your day

DO THIS TODAY

APPOINTMENTS

SHOPPING LIST

TO DO LIST

GOALS

The Daily Plan Challenge invites you to take a few minutes each day to plan your day for 30 days. Planning your day helps you get the most important things done, giving you a sense of accomplishment and making you feel more in control. Even the best plans can get derailed. However, having a plan in the first place will prepare you better for the unexpected, helping you adjust and overcome the obstacles.

You can plan your day the night before or at the start of your day—whatever works best for you. As you follow your plan, you can analyze your progress and make sure you're distributing time the way you want to. Or, if something interrupts your plan, you can reassess and make any adjustments. At the end of the day, you'll have a record of your accomplishments. You'll have a great feeling of satisfaction as you check tasks off a list and see all that you've achieved.

Mental

Express**Thanks**

20 thank you notes

The Express Thanks Challenge invites you to write 20 handwritten thank you notes within the next 30 days—an average of five per week—pushing you to thank people you might not normally thank. This may seem old fashioned, but a handwritten thank you note can express appreciation more fully than by text, email, or even face to face. You will feel a deep sense of gratitude as you write out the message and the recipient will feel valued to know you took the time to ponder, write, and mail the note.

While expressing thanks may seem as if it only benefits others, we also personally experience some amazing benefits. We become happier, less stressed, and more forgiving. When we develop a mindset of gratitude, we can become more empathetic and have stronger relationships. Buy some note cards, get out a pen, and see how good it feels to write thank you notes.

FamilyNight

4 evenings with your family

The Family Night Challenge invites you to spend time with your family four evenings in the next 30 days. It's easiest if you choose the same night each week; a night when everyone is free. Keep it simple. Enjoy dinner together as a family, watch a fun movie, whip up a favorite treat to eat, play games, or just sit around and talk. Rotate who chooses what you're going to do that week. If you don't live with family at the moment, find a group of friends that would like to gather regularly.

With the fast pace of life these days, it's easy to let weeks, even months, pass by without having any quality family time. When you plan specific times to get together, you will strengthen the bonds with your children. Studies show that children who get quality time with their parents communicate more openly, do better in school, and are less likely to have behavioral problems or become involved with drugs. You don't need to plan anything fancy or expensive—just take some time to enjoy each other as a family once a week. This may be the best investment you'll ever make.

Mental

Family Ties

Spend 300 minutes with family

The Family Ties Challenge invites you to spend 300 minutes with family (or close friends) over the next 30 days. What you do doesn't matter, just do it together. Eat together, play together, cook together, or work together. If you don't have any family around, spend the time with your friends. Gathering together with people you love builds emotional ties and lifelong memories. It will enable you to better face the challenges of life and to make good choices that lead to greater happiness.

A healthy social life has been proven to improve both your physical and mental health, but spending time specifically with your own family goes far beyond that. It leads to strengthened bonds between family members and more unity in marriage. Getting together with your children helps them perform better in almost every area of their lives. Having regular visits with elderly relatives can reduce their chance of age-related diseases and can add depth and joy to your life. Improve the quality of your life and spend more time with your family.

Free**Advice**

Meet with a mentor

The Free Advice Challenge invites you to find a mentor and meet with them six times over the next several months. A mentor is an experienced and trusted advisor who is willing to help you work toward a defined goal. Look for someone who has the kind of life and work ethic you'd like to have. It should be someone you truly respect, who could be a powerful role model. Think beyond former bosses and professors. Consider family members, friends, neighbors, spiritual leaders, and community leaders.

You can arrange a monthly lunch, a quarterly phone call, an occasional game of golf, or just a steady email correspondence. The best way to satisfy this challenge is to meet your mentor in person, even periodically, if possible. To make your meeting efficient, have questions ready and be sure to express your thanks for their time. Remember, a mentor's purpose isn't to direct everything you do; it is to offer guidance and provide feedback. However, you still need to think things through and make decisions for yourself. This balance is what fosters a healthy relationship with your mentor.

GameNight

Play group games

The Game Night Challenge invites you to play games with your friends or family four times in the next 30 days. You get to choose the game, who you will play with, and where you will meet. You can play cards, board games, video games, bowling, golf, or any other kind of game. For many people, the real challenge is scheduling a time each week that can actually work for everyone, but it will be worth it. While you may not continue having game nights this frequently after the challenge, the goal is to remind you of how refreshing and fun it is to play with others and hopefully get you to do it more often.

With our busy lives, we don't have the time to play with others like we used to as children. This makes us miss out on some very significant benefits that group play provides. Play reduces stress levels, exercises the brain, and boosts creativity. When we're together with others, we build relationships that can help stabilize and provide balance in our lives. Best of all, it's fun! Schedule your next game night today and savor one of the simple pleasures of life.

GetSmart

Learn for 500 minutes

The Get Smart Challenge invites you to learn something new or learn more about something you are interested in (one topic of your choosing) for 500 minutes during the next 30 days (17 min/day). Research a topic. Work on a skill. Practice playing an instrument. When was the last time you spent that much time focusing on a single topic? Most of us haven't done this outside of a classroom setting. If you meet this challenge, over the course of 30 days you will spend more than eight hours learning about one topic—perhaps becoming a quasi-expert in the area.

Curiosity is a natural human trait, and experts say the more we are interested in learning new things, the better we will be able to handle the situations we face each day. Asking questions and discovering things we didn't know before make us more flexible and adaptable. This much learning will require you to go deeper than just an Internet search. You'll most likely have to crack some books to get up to the 500 minutes. It's kind of like a treasure hunt where the prize is knowledge.

Mental

Good**Deed**

30 random acts of kindness

Mental

The Good Deed Challenge invites you to do 30 random acts of kindness over the next 30 days. Hold the door for someone, do the dishes, give up your seat on the bus or train, or pay someone a compliment. There are always opportunities to help others, and it's often the small things that have the greatest impact on others. In fact, that's the goal of the challenge—to turn your focus outward and make yourself more aware of the things you can do every day to help people.

While your reasons for helping others may be selfless, did you know when you help others you actually help yourself, too? Showing kindness can instantly boost your mood. People who are kind are well-liked and more successful—and may even live longer. In fact, studies show that even just setting a goal to be kind can make you happier. Look for opportunities each day to do good deeds and make the world a happier place.

HelpingHand

Serve others for 300 minutes

The Helping Hand Challenge invites you to look for opportunities to serve others for at least 300 minutes in the next 30 days (an average of 1 hour and 15 min/week). Most of us would love to serve others more often. The trick is figuring out what you can do. Consider the following: volunteer at a soup kitchen, do someone else's chores, talk to someone who's lonely, pick up trash, make cookies to give away, or invite someone over for dinner.

In our busy lives, it's easy to focus on fixing our own issues and problems and forget that we're surrounded by people who need our help. When you help others, you actually help yourself. Studies show when we reach out to those around us, we have a better sense of purpose and direction. We become more content and less stressed. By serving others, you may be surprised to discover your own life doesn't need so much fixing after all.

Mental

KindWords

Don't criticize

GOOD JOB!

The Kind Words Challenge invites you to only say kind words about other people for 30 days. It always feels uplifting to say something nice to another person, yet we often find ourselves doing just the opposite when we dwell on others' weaknesses. Even if we think we're being helpful or think what we're saying is honest, unkind words are not good for anyone. Remind yourself that no one is perfect. Over the next 30 days, if you catch yourself criticizing someone, say something kind about that person right away to redeem yourself (and to redeem that person).

Positive words and thoughts tend to crowd out negative ones, making us and those around us less stressed, happier, and more productive. Are you worried that people won't improve without your feedback? Amazingly, studies show that others actually change more for the good when they receive positive feedback. Perhaps your simple act of sharing a few kind words could make that person's day. Your words could even be something they cherish and remember for the rest of their life.

Lights**Out**

Go to bed at the same time

The Lights Out Challenge invites you to go to bed at the same time (± 30 min) each evening for 30 days. We all love the feeling of a good night's sleep, and there are some simple things that could help with this. Setting a consistent bedtime can help you sleep better. If you also set a specific time to get up every morning—ideally 7–9 hours after you go to sleep, you'll ensure that you get plenty of rest. Not getting enough sleep has been proven to impair performance, concentration, and memory the next day. Sleep deprivation can also make you overeat and feel irritable.

Keeping your bedtime consistent may be difficult, but it's worth the effort. Scientists have found that people with inconsistent sleep patterns had a raised pulse rate and increased levels of harmful stress hormones, which lead to a higher risk of heart problems. Getting enough sleep with a consistent bedtime allows the heart and mind to rejuvenate. Best of all, being fully rested helps you feel better and enjoy life more.

Mental

Looking**Good**

Dress for success

The Looking Good Challenge invites you to dress nicer than you normally would for 20 out of the next 30 days. You get to decide what "nicer" means. The goal is to try wearing nicer clothes to see if you like how it feels. You don't have to buy a new wardrobe to dress nicer. Look at what you have in your closet and see what outfits you can come up with. Simply adding accessories (like a belt, jacket, scarf, or necklace) can dress up clothing that might normally look casual. We may be more comfortable in today's casual world, but have we left behind some of the benefits of yesterday's more formal attire?

Dressing nicely gives you more confidence and generates more respect from those around you. A well-put-together outfit shows that you care about yourself and what you represent—in what you wear and in everything that you do—and gets you noticed in a positive way. Dressing well can even make you more productive at work. Nice clothes that fit properly are not only more flattering, but also serve as a gentle reminder to keep your weight in check. Prepare to be complimented, because when you pay more attention to how you dress, others will notice how nice you look and tell you so.

Lunch**Buddy**

10 lunches with others

The Lunch Buddy Challenge invites you to enjoy ten lunches with ten different people in the next 30 days (about 2 lunches/week). You can bring your own lunch or dine out. Invite anyone you'd like. Call an old friend. Grab your boss or co-worker. Take out the new employee. Go out as a group. The important thing is to spend time socializing, which is good for your physical and mental health. You'll find that your day goes faster as you anticipate lunch in the morning and then savor the fun you had during the afternoon.

When we get together with others, we connect about the challenges common to all of us and share experiences that help us gain a new perspective. We become more balanced and feel better about ourselves. It is significantly better to spend time with people in person, as opposed to through social media. In this way, we can read body language, observe mannerisms, and appreciate someone's personality. We can then respond in real time, which expands our thought processes, empathy, and enjoyment.

Mental

MeditationMaster

Meditate for 150 minutes

Mental

The Meditation Master Challenge invites you to meditate a total of 150 minutes during the next 30 days (just 5 min/day). Meditation will help you become more present, grateful, and aware. It sounds simple, but this is a powerful medicine that can make some of your worst physical and mental problems literally evaporate. Besides reducing stress, meditation can have other physical benefits, like boosting immunity, reducing inflammation, and decreasing pain. Meditation can also sharpen your memory and improve your attention span. As you become more aware of yourself and your surroundings, you will focus on others more which will lead to a more meaningful life.

Feel free to meditate using any technique you like, but here's a basic meditation: Sit up tall with your spine straight, either in a chair or on the floor. Close your eyes or just gaze softly downward. Breathe slowly and fully through your nose. As thoughts go through your mind, return your focus to the sensation of your breathing. Start by meditating for five to 10 minutes at a time. Set a timer to let you know when you're finished. Alternatively, you can do guided meditation via mobile app or a live class. Give meditation a try and see what it does for you.

NiceJob

List the good in others

The Nice Job Challenge invites you to write down three things each day that you like about other people. Simply write down a name and something you like about that person. By the end of the month, you will have a list of 90 positive, uplifting things that you have noticed about those around you. As you focus on people's good attributes, their shortcomings will fade into the background and will eventually go unnoticed.

It's natural to spend time thinking about what we don't like about others and what they should do to change. However, research shows that recognizing the strengths in others is much more effective in changing behavior than attacking their weaknesses. When you recognize the good in others, they feel valued, and they will work harder to continue to build their strengths. Perhaps even more importantly, as you fight the instinct to notice the negative in others, it's like draining a poison from your system. Your stress level will go down, and life will become a much happier, enjoyable journey.

Mental

Night Out

Go out 4 times

The Night Out Challenge invites you to go out with your friends and/or significant other four times in the next 30 days, or once a week. Technically you don't have to go out. You can have a night in at your house. The important thing is getting together with others because socializing and relaxing have tremendous health benefits. For even greater benefits, be sure to plan ahead, since anticipating the event can be almost as enjoyable as the event itself.

Relationships are what make life rich and satisfying—the more we invest in them, the greater the return. Deep relationships provide a source of love and support that will sustain us through thick and thin. Studies show that people who are married or enjoy long-term friendships are happier and lead a more balanced, healthy life. So plan a night out together and help your relationships grow.

PayItForward

Help someone in a big way

The Pay It Forward Challenge invites you to help one person in a big way. Paying it forward may traditionally involve helping three people, but starting with one person can be great and is a lot less overwhelming. You get to determine what "a big way" means. If the person wants to pay you back for what you've done, you need to insist that they "pay it forward" instead.

Most of us would like to help someone in a big way, but doing something so substantial may be intimidating. When you are deciding what to do, listen to your heart and trust your impressions. By accepting this challenge, you could literally change someone's life. Imagine how that would feel. There's a good chance that the life you change the most is your own.

Mental

Picture|It

Visualize for 150 minutes

Mental

The Picture It Challenge invites you to practice the technique of visualization for 150 minutes over the next 30 days (an average of 5 min/day). Just like athletes and performers, you can use visualization to help you do your best. Find a comfortable place. Take some slow, deep breaths and consciously relax the muscles in each area of your body. Then picture yourself doing something you wish you could do or that you'd like to do better. Pay attention to details and the feelings you experience as you are successful. Spend 5–20 minutes each session.

Mental imagery is used by politicians, surgeons, and even business executives to improve performance. You can mentally prepare yourself for all kinds of situations. Visualization can even be used to calm yourself down when you experience anger or stress (by picturing yourself responding peacefully). Focused thinking can be a big step toward reaching your inner potential. When you picture yourself succeeding, you accept it as possible, which is half the battle.

PlayList

Create 4 music playlists

The Play List Challenge invites you to create a music "first aid kit" by compiling four playlists. Like different size bandages, each playlist should address a specific need. Here are four suggestions, but feel free to change it up and make it your own to suit your needs: (1) music that relaxes you, (2) music that energizes you, (3) music that makes you happy, and (4) music that helps you think. You can decide how many songs are on each playlist, but 30–60 minutes for each is a good target.

Music can be a very powerful medicine. You could be totally burned out, then hear the right song and your energy level and outlook can change almost instantly. The opposite is also true. If you are agitated or anxious, the right music can calm you in minutes. By having these playlists ready to go, you'll be ready next time you need some emotional first aid. Whether you're at home, at the office, in your car, or out for some exercise, just start your playlist when you need it the most and let the music do the work. It's almost miraculous what music can do.

Mental

Play Time

Play for 300 minutes

The Play Time Challenge invites you to play for 300 minutes over the next 30 days (only 10 min/day). When you were young you probably played every day In fact, most parents made sure their children had a chance to play each day. At what age did playing become optional or, for some, even obsolete? Playing is important no matter what age you are. It exercises your mind and body and provides an opportunity to be creative. Playing creates an environment where we can socialize in a natural, unique way.

Embrace the child within you and go play. Play a fun sport like tetherball or dodge ball. Play a new board game. Even playing a video game is fine every now and then. Try a coloring book. Work on a puzzle. Build something cool with Legos. If you have children, play with them. If you don't, volunteer to watch a friend's child. After all, children are the experts when it comes to playing. Give it a try. It will breathe fresh life into you and help you perform at new levels.

QuoteMe

Memorize 10 quotes

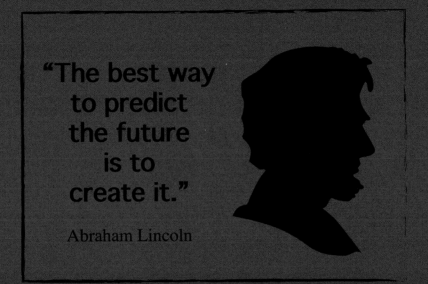

"The best way to predict the future is to create it."

Abraham Lincoln

The Quote Me Challenge invites you to memorize 10 quotes in the next 30 days. Choose something that interests you—quotes from someone famous, words from a song or poem, or a passage from a book or scripture. The quotes can be long or short. You decide, but make it a challenge for yourself.

Memorizing quotes will provide some good exercise for your brain. Memorization actually trains your brain to remember, increasing your ability to quickly process, store, and retrieve information. Having more memory capacity can make you a better learner since learning requires you to hold several concepts in your mind at once. More memory capacity also frees your mind to be more creative. Memorization increases your ability to focus, which also increases your ability to tackle difficult tasks. Having some handy quotes at the tip of your tongue might even make you look like a genius. Give it a try and see what memorization can do for you!

Mental

ShutDown

No media one hour before bed

Mental

The Shut Down Challenge invites you to avoid any kind of media one hour before bed for 25 out of the next 30 days. This means turning off anything with a screen—computers, tablets, phones, and television—at least one hour before you go to bed. If you can get everyone in your household to be on board, it will be easier. Set a time that all devices will be turned off. Consider removing computers and TVs from the bedrooms. Charge your devices in a separate room if that helps avoid the temptation to turn them back on. Make the hour before bedtime a time to reconnect with the people you love, talk about events of the day, read a book, or play a game—and get ready to shut down.

Studies show that media use before bed makes it more difficult to fall asleep and stay asleep during the night, and can negatively affect one's daytime alertness. In addition to the mental stimulation associated with screen time, the light emitted from the screens themselves mimics daylight. This interrupts the body's normal nighttime release of melatonin, which is a key ingredient for a good night's sleep.

Smile Big

Make 60 people smile

The Smile Big challenge invites you to get 60 different people to smile in the next 30 days (two people per day). That's right—60 different people, so you have to be constantly on the lookout for someone new to entice to smile. If you lose track and count someone twice, that's fine. When you smile at someone else, what ends up happening? Most people will smile right back. How do you both feel? Most likely, better than you did before. You've made a positive connection and that feels good. Think about how much nicer the world would be if people always smiled at one another.

Studies demonstrate that there are actual physiological changes that occur in our bodies when we smile—chemicals are released in our brains that make us happy and reduce stress hormones. Interestingly, your smile doesn't even have to be genuine to achieve this effect. Give it a try and see how you feel.

Mental

Stop**Think**
Reflect for 300 minutes

Mental

The Stop Think Challenge invites you to spend 300 minutes reflecting during the next 30 days (10 min/day). You pick how you would like to reflect on your life. You can meditate, pray, ponder, plan, journal, write letters, blog, play the piano, walk, or spend time in nature. The goal is to slow down, take a step back, and ponder your life, what you are thankful for, what you have learned, and what you can change to make life better.

Reflecting is one of the best ways to recharge. When you take time to reflect, you become less stressed, more grateful, more forgiving, better at working with others, and generally happier. Reflection is also good for your brain—it improves your memory and your ability to focus. You'll even have more self-control. When we take time to ponder, we can generate some of our greatest ideas—including ways we could make improvements in our lives. Stop and think from time to time and see what it does for you.

Sweet**Dreams**

Track how much you sleep

The Sweet Dreams Challenge invites you to track how much sleep you get each night for 30 days. Knowing how much you sleep is a key step to making sure you're getting enough (7–9 hours for adults). As you log how much you sleep each night, you may notice some patterns that affect your sleep. For example, do you sleep better after reading a book or after watching TV? Does going to bed late one evening affect your sleep the next evening? Do you sleep better with the house warmer or cooler?

Not getting enough sleep has effects that go way beyond feeling tired the next day— consequences that can't be masked by a cup of coffee. When you are asleep, your body repairs itself, produces hormones crucial for good health, and renews your mind. Lack of sleep can actually lead to heart disease, stroke, diabetes, arthritis, and other chronic conditions. Not getting enough sleep is associated with weight gain. Track your sleep and make sure you get a good night's rest. Besides feeling better, you will perform at your peak.

Mental

Tidy Up

Declutter for 300 minutes

The Tidy Up Challenge invites you to spend 300 minutes decluttering your life (about 10 min/ day). Tidy up your desk. Clean out a drawer. Get rid of clothes you don't wear. Organize the files on your computer. You can choose what you want to declutter. You'll find that decluttering lowers stress, gives you more energy, and makes it easier for you to focus. You might think you don't have enough time for this, but being organized can actually save you time in the end.

When you go to a spa, the decor is simple, clean, and open. There's a reason for this; an environment that is relaxing and inspiring makes you feel better. Imagine if your surroundings were simple, clean, and open. How much better would you feel? You'd feel more grounded and better able to focus on the people around you or the task at hand. This is the power of the decluttered life. What will you tidy up first?

Write|t
Journal for 20 days

The Write It Challenge invites you to keep a journal for 20 days during the next 30 days. It doesn't matter if you use a computer or paper and pen. You can write for as little or as long as you'd like. The goal is to see what journaling can do for you. Don't worry about grammar or punctuation. Don't spend too much time thinking about what to write—just let your stream of consciousness flow. Keep it private so you can write about whatever you want without worrying about what other people will think. Journaling could be the best (and cheapest) therapy you can give yourself.

Journal writing will help you process the thoughts and feelings you experience each day, reducing stress and helping you sleep better. As you write, you will get to know yourself better and will be able to figure out how to solve problems more effectively. Writing will exercise your brain and can increase your creativity. Writing can even help you become healthier physically. By keeping a record of your thoughts, you will be able to see your development and growth over time. Journaling may be the "write" thing for you!

Mental

You**Rock**

30 sincere compliments

Mental

The You Rock Challenge invites you to give 30 sincere compliments to different people during the next 30 days. Sure, you could sincerely tell a bunch of people that they look nice, but instead, challenge yourself to think of something really meaningful to say to each person. You'll both be better for it. Thirty different people is a challenge too. The goal is to get you in the habit of thinking of something nice you can say about every person you interact with. Imagine being able to continue this pattern after the challenge—sending good vibes out to everyone you meet.

When you look for the good in others, you will appreciate them more and overlook their shortcomings. When you give a compliment, you make the world a better place—better for the other person and better for you. The good feelings that result may even extend to the people you both come in contact with next. Did you know that positive feedback motivates people to change more than negative feedback does and that positive feedback can motivate people even more than money? Best of all—compliments are free!

Brown**Bag**
Pack your lunch

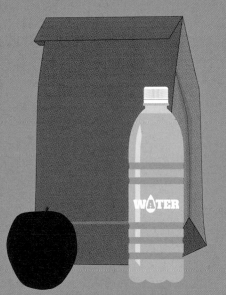

The Brown Bag Challenge invites you to pack a lunch for work for the next 30 days. Yes, it's like being in school again, only now you get to decide what to put in your lunch instead of your mother. The goal is twofold: first, when you pack your own lunch it tends to be healthier, and, second, you can save a lot of money by bringing your own lunch to work. Give it a try. It's not as hard as you think, and you may lose a couple pounds in the process.

The biggest obstacle for most people is finding the time to prepare a lunch, but consider how much time it takes to go out and get lunch during the workday. Most likely, it will take you less time to make a lunch in the morning than it will take you to go out and buy it during the day. Try storing your dinner leftovers in a container you can take to work so it's ready to go in the morning. If you have enough leftovers for two lunches, freeze one for another day. Throw a couple cans of soup in your desk drawer as a backup plan if you forget your lunch, run out of time, or even if the weather is bad. Get ready for a month of the best lunches you've ever had!

Nutrition

Financial

CharitableGift

Donate more

The Charitable Gift Challenge invites you to increase the amount of money you give to charitable organizations. This can be for your church, local school, fire department, a veterans fund, a campaign fund, or whatever organization you want to support. All that you have to do is contribute more in aggregate than you did last year. Setting up an automatic contribution makes it easy.

Interestingly, those who regularly donate to charities are more financially stable. This probably isn't because they have more money. It's likely due to the fact that they are better at managing their money. Giving to a charity can also help you feel more connected to the receiving organization. Help your favorite charity—and don't forget to get a receipt because if you itemize your taxes, you can declare your donation as a charitable contribution and get tax dollars back in your pocket.

Mental

Financial

Drop Pop
No soda pop

The Drop Pop Challenge invites you to give up soda pop for 30 days. This includes all types of sodas: regular, diet, and caffeine-free. Although soda might taste great, it's not great for your body or your pocketbook. Water, whether sparkling or still, is the best replacement beverage, but milk and tea are also good alternatives. Whatever you do, just drop the pop!

Regular soda is full of sugar or high fructose corn syrup, which makes it high in calories and low in nutritional value. Artificial sweeteners such as aspartame or saccharin might seem tame because they have virtually no calories, but they may cause health problems. The phosphoric acid in soda (not found in sparkling water) is bad for your teeth and your bones. Caffeine is added to some beverages keeps you coming back for more (and more!), and it carries it's own set of health risks. Do yourself a favor: Save some money and your health at the same time: drop pop.

Nutrition

Financial

FrugalChef
Dine for less

Nutrition

Financial

The Frugal Chef Challenge invites you to track your food expenses for 30 days. Use an app or a piece of paper. It doesn't matter. Just figure out how much you spend on food in the next 30 days. This includes groceries and eating out, including coffee and other snacks. The goal is to help you realize how much you actually spend on food. Since food is typically one of our largest expenses, it's amazing how much money you can save on food if you need to.

Sometimes just tracking how much you spend on something makes you more disciplined with your purchases. Remarkably, as you reduce your spending on food, the quality of the food you eat will most likely go up—since you'll dine out less and buy more inexpensive, basic foods like fruits, vegetables, beans, and grains. Eggs or oatmeal are both low-cost breakfast choices when you eat them at home. Packing your own lunch will save you money as well. For dinner, keep some simple meals (like pasta or chili) on hand. When you do have time, make a big batch and freeze some for later. Take the challenge and see how much money you can save!

Frugal Diner
Dine in

Nutrition

The Frugal Diner Challenge invites you to prepare your own food and dine in for at least 20 of the next 30 days. That means no take-out food or restaurants, including your favorite coffee house—a true challenge for some. This will save you more money than you probably realize and will improve the quality of food you eat. The goal of this challenge is to get you to dine in more than you usually do, even after the challenge is complete. Get ready for some good home-cooked food and start thinking about what you'll do with the money you save, not just this month but for months to come!

Some people may feel that cooking is difficult and time consuming, but it can also be a lot of fun. There are many meals you can cook, eat, and clean up in less than the time it takes to go to a restaurant and back! Take some time on the weekend to plan, shop, or even cook for the upcoming week. Whether you decide to keep dinner simple or whip up something wonderful, make big batches and save the extras for another day. With a little research and creativity, you'll be eating like a king and saving money along the way!

Financial

Good**Plan**

Check your service plans

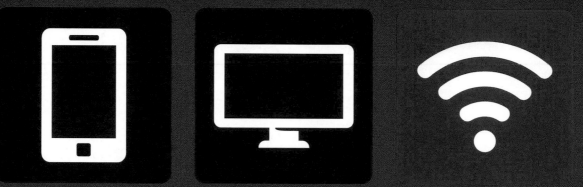

The Good Plan Challenge invites you to make sure you are on the best plans for your home phone, Internet, mobile phone, cable, music, and video subscriptions, etc. It may take some time to research, but it's not hard, and you can probably save hundreds of dollars. Providers frequently update their plans to remain competitive, but they don't tell you. However, they are usually happy to work with you if you give them a call. Circumstances in your life may even warrant a change to your services. For example, maybe you don't need a landline anymore or perhaps you don't watch cable like you used to.

Do a little research to compare services. For some services, you may want to call and ask for a competitive quote. Don't be afraid to dig a little and ask some questions to try to get what you're looking for. Sometimes you can get a great deal on your first year with a new service provider— but before you switch, check with your existing service provider because they may match the deal without the hassle of switching. You may be surprised how much you can save!

Financial

Good**Stuff**

Donate old stuff

The Good Stuff Challenge invites you to search through your closets and find old stuff (or maybe even new stuff) that you can donate to a local thrift shop. You'll have more room in your closets, more space in your rooms, and you'll feel good inside. In addition to pairing your goods with those who need them, most thrift shops also provide jobs for those in need.

If you don't have time to drop off your stuff (or a vehicle to haul it in), many donation-based organizations will come by and pick it up for free. Also, be sure to check the thrift shop's policy on acceptable items. Some allow most anything in good (or working) condition. Other organizations have more limits. You'll also want to ask for a receipt. If you itemize your taxes, you can include your donation as a charitable contribution and receive a tax benefit for your good deed.

Mental

Financial

HardTimes

Donate food

The Hard Times Challenge invites you to donate non-perishable food to a charity. You could complete this challenge by donating a can of soup, but why not make it more than that? Giving touches not only the person receiving, but it also warms your heart in a miraculous way. Think of it as helping others eat a decent meal who might not otherwise get one. When selecting the items to donate, think about what you would want if someone gave you a bag of groceries. Or if you prefer, donate cash instead.

Figure out what you spend on food for a day, week, or month and donate that much food. Sponsor a family for the holidays through a local organization. Donate at the grocery store to your local food bank. Send much more to the school canned food drive than you ever have before. Simple adjustments to your weekly finances can free up more than enough funds to make a significant contribution. In the process, you'll find that you have a firmer grasp on your own finances and you'll feel good knowing that you're making a difference in someone else's life.

Hold**On**

Wait before you buy

The Hold On Challenge invites you to wait seven days before making any optional purchases for 30 days. When you want to buy something that is outside the realm of your usual, necessary purchases, write it down with the date. Seven days later, if you still want to buy it, then go for it! This simple form of delayed gratification will help you spend less money and enjoy the things you do end up buying even more. As far as what's an optional purchase, that's up to you to figure out.

A multitude of studies indicate that up to 40% of purchases are bought on impulse. Marketers exploit this consumer weakness with discount offers and product placement to encourage impulse buying. They know that if they don't draw you in on the impulse buy, their chances of getting you to spend money with them are greatly reduced. If you can't pass up a deal, buy it, but keep it in the bag for a week so you can return it if you realize you really don't need it. Put this habit to the test this month and see if you end up getting more of what you really want.

Mental

Financial

Home**Brew**

Skip the coffee house

The Home Brew Challenge invites you to skip the coffee house for 25 of the next 30 days. Instead, brew your own coffee at home or at the office. Not only does home-brewed coffee save you money, it can be better for you depending on how you prepare it. Coffee shop coffee can have up to twice the amount of caffeine. Also, fancy, store-bought coffee drinks are often full of sugar and cream.

Try setting up the coffee pot so it's ready to brew the night before. You can whip up your own home brew in far less time than it takes to go to a coffee shop and wait in line. Get yourself a nice travel coffee mug. It will stay warm longer and will be much better than drinking from a paper cup. If you don't like the office coffee, get yourself a French press. Take the money you save and buy something you've been wanting, or better yet, save it!

InterestFree

Pay down your debt

The Interest Free Challenge invites you to increase your monthly payment for one of your loans or credit cards. You decide how much. Determine an amount that you can maintain until that debt is paid off. By making the commitment to pay down your loans more quickly, you'll save money on interest, pare down your debt, and reduce your stress level. You can save the most money if you pay more on the debt with the highest interest rate. You can also choose to work on the loan with the lowest principal to free up your cash flow. Either way, you will feel a sense of freedom as your debt shrinks and eventually disappears.

Debt is a heavy burden. It's like being in bondage with an unrelenting master—causing you stress and potentially harming your physical health. There's nothing like the feeling of freedom you get when you pay off a loan. You feel light and at ease! You have a fresh start to manage your money without that burden hanging over you. Reducing your debt will help your confidence grow and can lead to greater success in your career and your relationships.

Financial

Lost**Interest**

Check your loan rates

The Lost Interest Challenge invites you to check the interest rate for each of your loans to make sure you are getting the best possible rate. Rates change and so does your financial situation and credit score, sometimes allowing you to qualify for a lower rate. If you haven't checked your loan rates in a while, you may be able to save hundreds or even thousands of dollars.

If you have a home loan, a mortgage broker is probably your best source for understanding if you have a better option. For other debt, such as student loans or credit card debt, your bank can give you advice. Investigate a bit and see what you can save. Even if you don't find a better rate, you'll learn a little more about how the process works and will have peace of mind knowing you already have the best deal.

Financial

Meal**Plan**

Plan your meals

The Meal Plan Challenge invites you to plan your meals for 30 days. Ideally, you should plan your meals each week and only buy your groceries once a week. However, even if you just plan one day in advance, that's fine too. You can go out to eat (or order take-out) so long as it's part of your plan. As you become better at meal planning, you will find that you spend less, save time, waste less, and eat better.

When you follow a plan, you're less likely to buy fast food and you're more efficient when shopping for groceries. You're also more likely to cook your own food, which is usually healthier than prepared foods. Make it fun (and simple) by giving a theme to different days of the week—like fish Friday, Mexican Monday, or pasta Tuesday. Write the plan on your calendar or use a meal planning app—even a piece of paper will do. Give it a try and say goodbye to the stress of constantly trying to figure out what you're going to eat.

Nutrition

Mental

Financial

MoneySpent

Create a budget

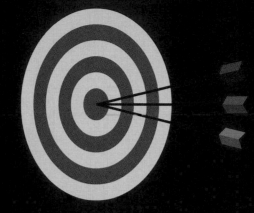

The Money Spent Challenge invites you to create an historical budget from the past three months. Gather your old bank statements and credit card statements and figure out how much you earned versus how much you spent in different categories. You can use paper, a spreadsheet, or an online tool. Don't forget to include annual expenses (like homeowner's insurance) by dividing the expense by 12 and including it in each month's expenses. Once you have compiled the numbers, figure out if you earn more that you spend each month.

This simple challenge can help you understand where your money is going. Empowered with this information, you may decide to change your spending habits to better align with your goals. When you are done with this challenge, consider doing the Penny Counter Challenge where you track your spending for a month to see if you can stick to your new plan.

No**Butts**

Attempt to quit smoking

The No Butts Challenge invites you to try to quit smoking. This is the most important thing you can do for your health. For most people, this will not be their first attempt as it usually takes several tries to quit smoking. Considering the price of tobacco, not to mention the obvious health risks , why not try again? Think about what you could buy with the savings even if you're not 100% successful. Each time you try to quit, even if you fail, you learn something that may help you be successful the next time. This may be the time that actually works for you!

Some people gradually reduce how often they smoke. Others go cold turkey. There is not a one-size-fits-all method to quitting. Nicotine patches and/or gums have been shown to increase success rates. Certain prescription medications have also demonstrated remarkable effects at reducing withdrawal symptoms. Many people find they do better when they have the support of a doctor, coach, or a smoking cessation program. Whatever you do, keep trying as it usually takes several attempts. Millions of people succeed at quitting every year. You can, too.

Nutrition

Financial

No Thanks

No alcohol

Nutrition

The No Thanks Challenge invites you to not drink any alcohol for 30 days. Whether you're looking to cut a few calories, moderate your drinking, or save a few bucks, the No Thanks Challenge can help. When was the last time you went 30 days without alcohol? Why not take the challenge and show yourself that you can do it? Even if you do continue drinking after the challenge, hopefully you'll drink less often.

Studies show that moderate alcohol consumption may have some benefits, but many experts agree that the risks from consuming alcohol outweigh the benefits. One aspect you may not want to give up is the socialization involved, a highlight for many adults. In social settings, try drinking sparkling mineral water, or mix sparkling water with juice in a wine glass. You can have just as much fun without the alcohol and spare the negative side effects. If it's too hard for you to resist alcohol at parties, get creative and plan a social event (like a hike) that doesn't include alcohol so you can still enjoy being with friends.

Financial

PennyCounter

Track what you spend

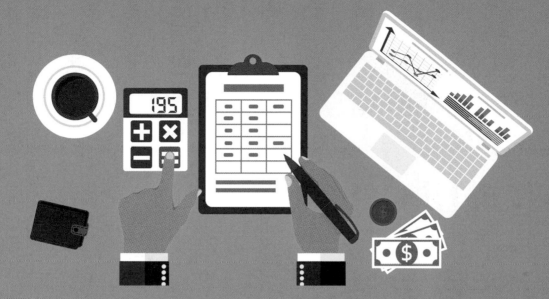

The Penny Counter Challenge invites you to track every penny you spend for the next 30 days. Track it on paper, on a spreadsheet, or online. Put every receipt in a box each time you come home to help you form the habit. The goal of this challenge is to categorize each item so you can better understand where your money goes each month. Knowledge is power. Once you know where your money is going, you can better optimize your spending.

Studies show that the more financially responsible you are, the less stress you will feel. Many Americans—even those with high incomes—are living paycheck to paycheck. Most of us know we need to be more disciplined, but don't know where to start. The first step is to track your spending. After that, you can devise a plan that works better for you financially. Often just the exercise of tracking where your money goes will help you spend more wisely and allow you to feel more in control of your life.

Financial

RiskyBusiness

Check your insurance rates

The Risky Business Challenge invites you to get one or more competitive insurance rate quotes for each type of insurance that you hold. This includes auto, home insurance, life, and any other type of insurance you may have. If you haven't checked your insurance rates in a while, you may be able to significantly reduce your premiums.

While you're checking, consider changing your deductible amounts. If your financial situation has improved, you may be able to afford a higher deductible in order to reduce your insurance rates. Also consider your coverage limits. What was a solid amount of coverage 10 years ago may not be enough today. Make sure to get a combined quote for home and auto as the combined coverage is often significantly less expensive. If your net worth is starting to grow, consider an umbrella policy to protect your assets against large claims. Speak to your insurance agent or do a little research on your own to explore your options.

Financial

Save Yourself

Increase the amount you save

The Save Yourself Challenge invites you to increase the amount you save each month. One of the best ways you can do this is to increase your monthly contribution to your employer-sponsored savings plan. However, if you haven't set aside an emergency fund (one or more months of income saved for a rainy day), you may want to start building this first. You could also add to your children's college savings fund.

Whatever you do, figure out a way to make the contribution automatic so you don't have to manage it. With money, you probably won't miss what you don't see. If you wait until the end of the month to see if you have enough money to save, it will already be spent. Pay yourself first (by saving). You'll certainly thank yourself later.

Financial

Work**Plan**

Set up family chores

The Work Plan Challenge invites you to set up a schedule for the household chores in your home. Having a set routine for keeping your home neat and tidy will contribute tremendously to the happiness and well-being of everyone living there. Along with a work plan, it's important to have a reward system to motivate and unite everyone who helps.

Teaching children to work and to manage money are two of the most valuable life skills parents can give their children. Don't have kids? For a healthier relationship with your spouse or significant other, mutually agree upon household responsibilities, then make sure you reward each other when those responsibilities are met. For example, how about simply ordering food in together to enjoy your nice clean home? No spouse or roommate? Set up a plan for regular cleaning and offer to exchange help with a friend (or friends) so you can do the work together. Not only will the work be more fun, but you can plan a night out together afterward.

Mental

Financial